A Hand
Through the Bars

Amanda Grafe

A Hand Through the Bars

Table of Contents

Welcome to the Asylum (Preface)

I never thought I would see the day
When things would turn out this way
The incident was out of our hands
As we, the staff, were undermanned
Well, they certainly got the better of us
Those committed to this house of nuts
Oh no! I can hear knocks at my door
It's one of the staff, begging no more
How could things go so astray?
Now, between padded walls I am here to stay
Again! The screams, oh, how silence lacks
As my door opens up a crack
In the shadows I manage to hide
Until help comes, I must stay alive

Church on the Hill

Hello, I work at the church on the hill
Here are your flowers and burial bill
I've dressed the corpse in velvety teal
And in the coffin, have had it sealed
In order to make them look like a king
I reduced costs by omitting the string
You see, the bell which indicates if one is dead
Is attached by string to the coffin bed
So, if the corpse were to move just a little
The string on its finger would start to wiggle
The vibration would travel through the string
And cause the bell to give a ring
Then just to be sure we would exhume the coffin
But to find one alive does not happen often
Now medical advances can correctly derive
Whether one is dead or alive
So, with all these new medical things
We can afford to do away with the string
What a mistake that had turned out to be
For when I awoke, for myself I could see
My morticians had listened to this old man
There is no string on my own hand

Thrashes in the Water

Thrashes in the water, I remember that day
When I went on the dock to pray
I just wanted to die alone
For someone to help, was a deed unknown
I knew very well I couldn't swim
It was my thrashes in the water that attracted him
My flailing arms must have been a distraction
For after a while he started thrashing
Down to the bottom of the lake he went
Where my time was intended to be spent
Now, every day I sit on the sand
Thinking about my failed plan
And how I would give every penny, every quarter
Wishing it had been I who saw thrashes in the water

Lucky Penny

I saw a penny as I was walking by
And I thought I'd leave it for another guy
I would have been happy to pick it up
But figured someone else needed the luck
I always think when you see a lucky penny
Well, you know, there aren't very many
And the penny isn't really meant for you
But for the next guy coming through
So, I passed it by and left it on the ground
And then ... a screeching sound

The next thing that I could see
Was a man standing next to me
"You were nearly killed by that car," he said.
"One second sooner, you would have been dead."

I looked at him, my face filled with despair
"I shouldn't have left that penny there.
I left if for the next fella who came by
Thinking he needed it more than I."

Then he laughed, "You do the same thing I do.
That's why I left that penny for you."

Death of a Poet

I have a talent, I guess you could call
I write poetry as I free fall
Yes, it's true, it inspires me
Falling above the earth and trees
Parachute lever in my hand
I even write as I land
For many find it hard to comprehend
The wonderous view as they descend
That is why I jot it down
Right before I hit the ...

Puddles

They're really bad, the streets outside
They will not allow for one bike ride
Most of the summer has been like this
Constant rain and high flood risks
The sewers have even overflown
Washing away covers, creating holes
But who cares, It's time for fun
Well for me, not for everyone
Not my mom, she tells me to stop
When in the puddles my feet drop
But on this day she has given in
And so the puddle jumping begins
Splash, splash, splash, mom isn't this fun
But there is no answer from anyone
I turn around and wait to see
Where my mom is hiding from me
Well, I don't know what went wrong
She was puddle jumping and then, gone
Come to find out, once stopped the rain
She was just playing dead in the drain

Crazy Scientist

There was a crazy scientist
Who had a crazy science wish
He wished that he would go so far
As proving a galactic war
So, every day he tried to find
Things to attest what was on his mind
Ironically to prove him right
He uncovered a massive, ancient, fight
Between those that looked like man
Except with large foreheads and bigger hands
And guess who was on the other side
Don't look at me, I was also surprised
You see, World War Three was World War One
And the invaders had already come
For the galactic war had indeed occurred
And the invaders were what we humans were

The Book

I've never seen a book before
That bleeds out of every pore
I'm not sure what kind of fable
Is sitting here on my table
I am so afraid of this book
Afraid to touch, afraid to look
Though I've closed the library to my guest
They insist on going on a quest
To find out what's all that noise
That sounds like crying girls and boys
The scariest is when I'm alone at night
My body freezes up with fright
I hear their screams through my home
And to the corridors I start to roam
I make my way towards the sound
Until my heart begins to pound
And though outside all is fine
It's what's going on between the spine
Now that is something to worry about
And what would happen if something got out?

A Light in the Tree

I can see a light in the tree
For some reason, it bothers me
I know of no other houses nearby
That is why the light caught my eye
I decided one day to take a look
But in the cold my body shook
So, I turned around and went inside
Instead to bed and closed my eyes
I saw it for a few days after that
While by the window I watched and sat
It's when the light went dim and black
That I decided to go back
Back to the forest to that same tree
Where many people were waiting to see
Down the branches a small body came
With no hope now of being saved
And in his hand, a small flashlight
That with time no longer burned bright
If only, one said, someone had seen
The light that for days had continued to gleam
They might have helped him out of this tree
And with us this boy would still be
So, as a tribute to the little child
I put up a light that burns all the while
To remind everyone, especially me
Of the light I ignored in the tree

Seagulls

Seagulls, Seagulls in the sky
For them it's time to say goodbye
Cock my gun and aim it high
Shoot that bird out of the sky
This is week twenty-one
Sitting here with my gun
Proves to be a hobby now
Watching seagulls falling down
I think I have shot every one
And it has been almost fun
For they deserve not to live
These dirty creatures, full of sin
To eliminate the world of filth
Somehow alleviates my own guilt
Because I am good for not much else
Except sitting here by myself
My hypocrisy, I am quite aware
If I gave half a mind to give a care
But when the day is over and through
I do what someone has to do
I keep to myself most of the time
My company consists of brandy and wine
Most weekends I spend here
With a belly of that and a belly of beer

And I will wait night and day
To dispose of those that fly my way
They've stopped coming around, fortunately
Maybe they've learned to let people be
And even if that is not the case
Their pathetic lives I must erase
Right now, I feel quite satisfied
That they have all gone and died
But my duty is not yet fulfilled
For on this earth is one more ill
I can feel it in the air
It is close, it is here
And if one more wretch exists still yet
Conveniently, one bullet left

The Picture

There is a picture that hangs above my door
It depicts an angel upon a marble floor
She sits there and sees my every move
And watches over me inside my room
Her face is sweet, devoid of tears
And she gives me hope, through all my fears
The way the paint mixes with soft pastel
She's my guardian angel, I can tell
Today I learned that my grandma was sick
I cried, wishing it was me God picked
"How sick?" I asked wiping my eyes.
"Very," I was told. "Last night she died."
To hide my sadness, I ran into my room
Hoping to wake up from this nightmare soon
And the picture that hangs above my door
Well, there is not just one angel there anymore

White (A Moment of Sanity)

White is a soft, puffy cloud floating in the sky
White is a snowflake greeting the tip of your nose
White is the fog that surrounds you
White is the sound of boots crunching against the earth (after all
    your friends have disappeared)
Red is the contrast against the snow
Red is the color of a scarf that is caught on a tree branch
Red is your heart pounding in your chest
Black is the silhouette of the man who drags me towards the ocean
    as I take my final breaths
Black is...

A Hand Through the Bars

If I could just squeeze my hand through these bars
Perhaps someone would see it from afar
Then for help they could call
And I would have more than no hope at all
You must know, the coffee is no good here
And trust me I need it in this career
But not even coffee can clear their heads
Even when restrained in their beds
The kicking, the screaming, like little kids
Until the needles help close their lids
And just when I think it is the end
They wake up and begin again

There is one girl, I can't say her name
She is the one of whom I am not ashamed
She has come very far since she first arrived
With several attempts at suicide
When I can't take this job any more
I go to her room and open the door
With compassion I take her hand
And we talk about a more pleasant land
I guess she enjoys my company too
Before I release her to the work of the crew
She doesn't like them, but she'll be fine
Once she takes her phenothiazines

She reminds me of why I chose this profession
On rare occasion, it can be a blessing
But my garden of desire to help those in need
Has since been overgrown with weeds
Still, the staff plays nice, nice
Hiding our pain of sacrifice
Yet, never has a patient been mistreated
Never scolded and certainly not beaten
That is why I don't understand
Why things got so out of hand

A meeting out of state left us a few men down
So the six of us had to make up ground
Tired, we were, and not on the ball
We left a patient to wander the hall
They let a few of their friends out
Ignoring orders we were forced to shout

In my room, a window with bars
I look through them for passing persons or cars
I'll take a breath, for help there's still time
Before they go and lose their minds
Wait, that's right, they already have
That's why we lock them in rooms with pads

But now it is me who is inside this room
Begging for someone to rescue me soon
The patients have already made their start
In ripping the doctors' flesh apart
We should have put the tools away
For with these the patients like to play
Then again! Screams through the wall
Oh God! I do not like this game at all
There is nothing I can say
To make these madmen go away
And if I dare make a sound
Well, I just might be found
So, I will sit here silent in my tomb
Deep inside this padded room
A white cloth, from my smock I rip hard
Then I stick my hand out through the bars

Whatever I do, I must not turn around
I'll hide in the shadow here on the ground
More, I can hear them again
Count ... seven, eight, nine, TEN!
The window on the door, it opens up
I fear more now than when it was shut
A small, skinny hand slips inside
And softly, but firmly, grabs hold of mine
Then in a voice, so very sweet
My words of assurance she does repeat

Mirror Image (A Moment of Sanity)

You're stupid

You're ugly

You're fat

You stink

You're a freak

You're a loser

You're scum

And a geek

You're dirt

You're gross

In fact, you're nothing at all

These were the things said to my friend, as I turned my back
and pretended not to see

And when I got home to my room, there was someone else
waiting for me

I asked their name

"Coward," they said. "That is my name."

Then I realized I was looking in the mirror and talking to my
own reflection

The Dryer

My child disappeared today
I don't know where she went
I checked the lakes and streams
And the cabin that we rent
I looked all around
Sideways, up and down
I fear my baby girl
Has somehow gone and drowned
Then when I could look no lower
And when I could look no higher
I found a trail of her clothes
That were leading to the dryer
I opened up the door
And found her little shoe
But there was no daughter
What was I to do?
Years have passed and gone away
To find her is my one desire
But I have a real hunch
That she is in the dryer

The Poem of the Insane

Lakhfiiahslklihfslinflwlwlihwi
Fslweflhhelpaflnaflapeihtiphm
Alfjeoacanafoaihteihyouafoiehf
HearoHELPoafoeihofjfijoffegtgg
alfhahfHIlgdlgaihHelpahfdhfdo
lafjdfhlafhafhHelpdfaofhaghag
aofhihaPLEAsehdhifohhioed
lfsdhaofhaoifhello?dfoaiffddggr

Tracks in the Snow

My friends and I went for a walk
Just for fun and to talk
The five of us in a line
Began to disappear one at a time
The four of us were really scared
When we saw tracks but no one there
So, we continued through the snow
Not sure of where we were to go
And as we made it on together
The worse got the snowy weather
The three of us tried to make it home
But lost in the woods we continued to roam
I'm not sure where we were right then
But the tracks started up again
The two of us shivered in fear
As the tracks continued to near
I don't know who is left with me
Through the fog I cannot see
I would turn around and check
But I am too scared, for I am next

The Boy and the Bunny

I once was perfect, with no seams torn
But years have passed, I am not like that anymore
I remember the paper, shiny and gold
Back when I was nice and new, not old

I was given to a child on Christmas Eve
Of all her gifts, she was with me the most pleased

She held me close through love, sadness and fright
Many days after Santa came that night
She took me to school, to the park, and to balls
And dolled me up in dresses, hats and shawls
But after a while, I didn't know what I had done
She locked me in a box, away from everyone

Suddenly, one day, it seemed like forever
I was taken from my box all worn and weathered
With happiness and cheer, my soul glowed
It was Christmas again, and outside it snowed

I was given to a small boy, so frail and weak
That a chair with wheels was his permanent seat
We had so much fun as we played inside on the rug
Oh, how good it felt to again be loved

But that night I found it hard to sleep
As he gave a cough with each heartbeat
And his breathing, sporadic and quick
His stuffy nose, he must have been sick

When I awoke in the morning, I lay alone in bed
With no boy, only an indentation from his head
It's because I am all weathered and torn
That's why he left, I said with scorn

I jumped to the floor, I ran away
He doesn't like me or else he would stay
I don't want to go back in the dark
I want to go with him to a ball or to the park

I hid outside, hoping he would look for me
But, it was his aunt who made my discovery
She brought me inside and made me clean
Washed my fur...sewed my seams

Then I was placed back in a box
Back in the black, back in the dark
The last thing I saw was a horrible sight
Many crying faces and then, night

I never got to go to another ball or to the park
Instead I am here again in the dark
But I don't mind it in the least
Because now I am with the boy and can be at peace

Only Fifteen

I am only fifteen, but that's alright
You look kind of good in the setting sunlight
I have never been within a hundred feet
But the way you slick your hair back is really neat
Your eyes are such a piecing brown
Inside their depths I could just drown
And your skin so bronze and soft
Your suit, a nice shade of moss
Your grin is straight, clothes without crease
My skin is too white, and I have crooked teeth
I bet the girls are all after you
But they probably don't have as high an I.Q.
I am good at school, I'll tell you that
Not a nerd and that's a fact
Well, at least not yet anyway
Until I got the news today
My doctor says I may need glasses
To see the board and pass my classes
So, I hope you like girls with specs
Silly blouses and socks with checks
I am so nervous, I hope you can't tell
Rehearsing my lines, under your spell
Here comes my mom with my glasses for me
To make it easier for me to see

Now let me just buff them with my sweater
So, I can put them on and see a bit better
You seem so lifeless from not so far away
Like you've been here forever since today
You look so familiar, from some time ago
Like from a famous movie or TV show
Eh ... I don't love you like before
I don't even like you anymore

Oh no, you've got to be kidding me
I preferred when I couldn't see
Your face, well, it's lost all its spark
You're just a statue of that guy in the park

Behind the Curtain

My grandma lay silently in her cot
Looking out the window at a view she liked a lot
She said she might not be here for very much time
And that she had to tell me what was on her mind

"Do you remember your grandfather?" my grandma asked.
"All I remember is when I saw him last,
I was very, very, small
And he would roll me my baby ball."

"Before I leave, remember one thing
It is the story of how I got my wedding ring
I loved your grandfather very much
I loved his smile, I loved his touch
He sold all he had to buy my wedding band
And the best day of my life was when he put it on my hand."

"I can't imagine anything like that," I said.
And with that, grandma turned her head
"You just wait, your day will come,
When all those loves are narrowed down to one
To share your laughter and your dreams
To hold you close and mend painful seams
And in this person, you will find your best friend
Someone to be with you until the end."

The man who lay next to us gave me a smile
It seemed he had been listening all the while
And when my grandma fell asleep
I snuck away through the curtain crease

The man asked, "Who is that in the other room?"
"My grandma. She's asleep, but she should be up soon.
Why are you here? You seem well."
"I am not sick at all," he said, "Is it easy to tell?"
A second time I asked, "Well, why are you here then?"
"Well, isn't it obvious? I am waiting for a friend.
I was sent here to make sure my friend
Made it safely from here home again."

With that he disappeared before my eyes
Past the ceiling and into the sky
So, I snuck back into grandma's room
Where I would tell her, when she woke up soon
But I couldn't wait so long to tell
So, I shook her arm and began to yell
And when I couldn't wake my grandma alone
I realized the man's friend had made it home
At least I got to see my grandpa again
And grandma was right he was a good friend
And under her pillow, a letter from her to him
This must be what true love is

The Corner

"What is on the tape?" he said.

A reply, "Of the boy that's dead.
Listen closely and you will find
Something to scare you out of your mind."

(Tape plays)

"I am recording myself here today,"
These things the boy does say,
"And in my room there is this thing
And of the north corner, it is king
Its shadow is there all the time
On its appearance, I dare not opine
Sometimes I have friends in here
But of company, it seems not to care
They see it too, they've told me
But to us all, it's a mystery
It has been there now for a year
And has never moved or shown fear
So, I will leave this recording drone
And see what it does when it's alone."

(Static)

"I am back in the room with nothing to hear
Do you think it sees me standing here?
Just to make sure, I'll poke it then...
Closing my eyes, counting when...

Still don't know what it is, but it won't do me harm
As long as I don't touch it, lest I lose my other arm."

Crows

Crows, black as night, they do land
On the graves with the praying hands
Trust me, I've been here for quite a while
Staring at my new grave tile
I ordered it the other day
Until the end of my life, here it will stay
Too prepared, one can never be
Even though my death is years from me
It's nice, it's made of marble stone
And is here on this plot alone
It would be better if not for the crows
And why they land here, no one knows
That is not true, the gravedigger says
They land on the graves of those soon to be dead
And as he scanned the cemetery
He looked back and smiled weakly, you see
Across the yard and under the tree
Was a crow on my stone, waiting for me

Escape from the Book

Whatever was in the book got out
And now I can hear more than ever its shouts
The only thing left between me and this thing
Are the library doors in the far west wing
I tried more than once to leave my home
But I am too feeble to make it out alone
So, I run for cover inside my room
Where I know it'll come for me soon
So quickly it does, a pound on the door!
How long will they hold until they hold no more?
And then they will break and let inside
God save my frail body and trembling mind!
But that is not all I worry about
I fear like the others it'll make me shout
From all the pain that is in store
Once that thing comes through the door

Help Arrives (Epilogue)

My friends and I would stand outside the asylum and throw rocks
    at the window
Tiny pebbles
We would try to get a rise out of the residents, but more often
    than not, the doctors would come outside and yell at us
But all was quiet today
No heckling from the patients, no patients to heckle
Outside one of the windows, a hand hung through the bars, a
    white flag between their fingers
Someone was calling for help
Probably just my ears playing tricks, but I had to check it out
The corridors were empty, bloody
Patients huddled and rocked themselves calm
No one approached me
I began to open the doors hoping to find someone in charge
The doctors who had once told us kids to stop fooling around outside
    lay still on the floor
Motionless
A nurse was in one of the rooms, barely noticeable among the
    shadows
Her neck was a gaping red abyss
There was a journal and some loose paper
It was filled with rhymes, scary stuff
It had almost inspired me to tell this story in a rhyme
But people who rhyme are crazy

About the Author

Amanda Grafe is an author / illustrator / artist from New England. She enjoys hunting for sea glass and spending time with her dog. In addition to *A Hand Through the Bars*, she is the author of three children's books and is an arts journalist. To learn more about her and her work please visit www.amandagrafe.com

Made in the USA
Columbia, SC
29 November 2020